Rounds, Glen
    The boll weevil, verses selected and illus.
Golden Gate, 1967.

1. Folk songs   I. T.

The BOLL WEEVIL

GOLDEN GATE JUNIOR BOOKS

San Carlos · California

The BOLL WEEVIL

Verses selected and illustrated by

GLEN ROUNDS

The first time I saw little Weevil

he was sitting on a cotton square –

The BOLL WEEVIL

The Boll Weevil is a mean little bug—

Came from Mexico, they say.

Came all the way to Texas, just looking for a place to stay.

Just looking for a home, yes, looking for a home.

The first time I saw little Weevil

He was on the Western Plain.

Next time I saw the Weevil he was riding a Memphis train.

He was looking for a home, just looking for a home.

When the Farmer saw those Boll Weevils

They were in his rocking chair.

The next time they were in his corn field and they had all their family there,

Just fixing up a home, yes, fixing up a home.

The Boll Weevil say to the Farmer,

"You can ride in that Ford machine,

But when I get through with your cotton you can't buy gasoline.

You won't have no home, won't have no home."

Oh, the Boll Weevil said to the Doctor,

"Better pour out all your pills."

When I get through with the Farmer he cain't pay no doctor's bills.

He'll have no home, he'll have no home."

The Farmer say to the Woman,

"What do you think of that?

Those devilish Boll Weevils have been eating my Stetson hat.

It's full of holes, it's full of holes."

The Merchant said to the Farmer,

"Well, what do you think of that?

If you'll get rid of the Weevil I'll give you a brand new Stetson hat.

He's looking for a home, just looking for a home."

The Farmer took little Weevil

And put him in Paris Green.

The Weevil said to the Farmer, "It's the best I've ever seen.

I'm goin' to have a home, a happy home."

The Farmer took the Boll Weevil

And put him in a frying pan.

Weevil said to the Farmer, "It's mighty warm, but I'll stand it like a man.

This will be my home, yes, this will be my home."

The Weevil grabbed the Farmer

And throwed him in the sand—

Put on the Farmer's overcoat and stood up like a natural man.

Said, "I'm going to have a home, a happy home."

The Boll Weevil said to the Farmer,

"You better leave me alone.

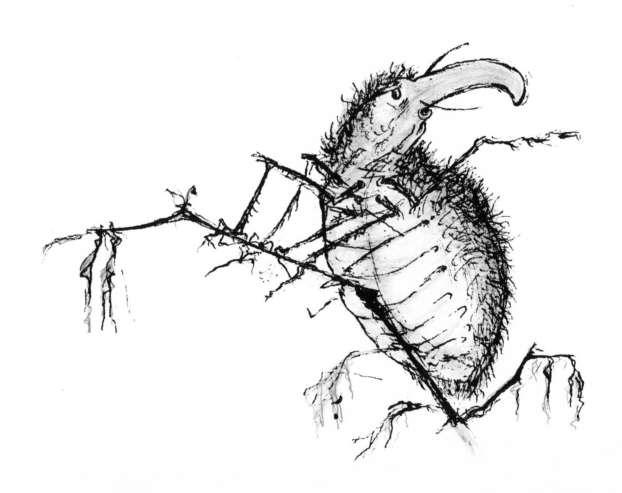

I done et up all your cotton, now I'm starting on your corn.

I'll have a home, yes, I'll have a home."

The Farmer said to the Merchant,

"I need some meat and meal."

"Get away from here, you son of a gun, you got Boll Weevils in your field.

Going to get your home, going to get your home."

The Farmer said to the Merchant,

"I didn't make but one bale,

But before I let you have that one I'll suffer and die in jail—

I'll have a home, I'll have a home!"

Well, the Merchant got half the cotton,

The Boll Weevils got the rest.

Didn't leave the poor Farmer's wife but one old cotton dress,

And it's full of holes, all full of holes.

The Farmer said to the Banker,

"We're in an awful fix.

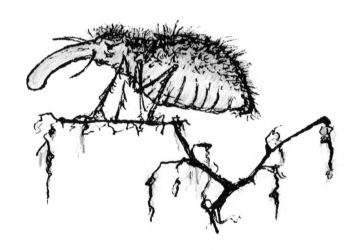

The Boll Weevil et all our cotton up and left us only sticks.

We've got no home, we've got no home."

The Banker was bad as the Weevils,

Said, "There's nothing I can do.

I can't lend you any more money for the Weevils might eat that too,

And leave it full of holes, all full of holes."

The Farmer said, "Come on, Old Woman,

And we'll travel out West.

The Weevils et up everything we've got but this old cotton vest,

And it's full of holes, all full of holes."

Now if anyone should ask you

Who it was that wrote this here song,

You can say it was just a homeless Farmer with ragged britches on,

Just hunting for a home, yes, hunting for a home.

THE BOLL WEEVIL

Arranged by Patty Zeitlin

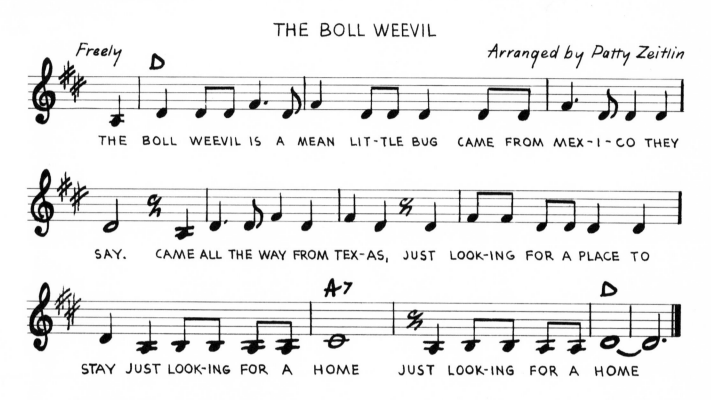

Music from the singing of Jake Zeitlin as he learned it from Carl Sandburg in the early 1920s

Glen Rounds, author-illustrator of more than a score of books for young readers, is a man with roots deep in the soil of America. Born in the Badlands of South Dakota, he has roamed the country from coast to coast—as ranch hand, cowpuncher, logger, mule skinner, carnival man and sign painter, to mention only some of his itinerant occupations. His diverting and at the same time ruefully perceptive drawings for this version of the ballad of the Boll Weevil reveal his observation and understanding of the small tenant farmer in his battle not only with boll weevils but with bankers, droughts, floods and credit merchants.

Like most folk songs, the precise origin of "The Boll Weevil" is shrouded in the mists of the past. It was inspired by the invasion of an army of boll weevils which crossed the Rio Grande from Mexico into Texas, then marched steadily at the rate of about forty miles a year across the entire South to the Atlantic seaboard, leaving havoc and consternation in its wake. Carl Sandburg made the words and music to the song known to the world many years later.